Nurse, Pastor, and Patient

Nurse, Pastor, and Patient

A Hospital Chaplain Talks with Nurses

By

GRANGER WESTBERG

Chaplain, University of Chicago Clinics
Associate Professor of Pastoral Care
Federated Theological Faculty, The University of Chicago

AUGUSTANA PRESS
ROCK ISLAND. ILLINOIS

NURSE, PASTOR, and PATIENT

[PRINTED
IN USA]

AUGUSTANA BOOK CONCERN
Printers and Binders
ROCK ISLAND, ILL.
1955

To
HELEN, MY WIFE,
My Understanding Counselor

Preface

IT IS the author's hope that every nurse who reads this book will want to try out some of the things suggested here in order that she may enjoy the experience of a new dimension in caring for people who are ill.

Illness affects the whole man—not only his physical body. Therefore every nurse ought to be equipped to deal more adequately with the spiritual needs of patients. This book seeks to give specific suggestions which the nurse may put into practice immediately.

I am greatly indebted to the Reverend Russell L. Dicks, a former teacher of mine, who pioneered in the field of nurse-minister relationships. He wrote a book in 1941 entitled *Who Is My Patient?* His book, which we use regularly in classes for nurses and which is thoroughly enjoyed by them, has encouraged me to believe that nurses would be interested in other aspects of the care of the spiritual needs of patients. I have tried, therefore, in this book to describe how the nurse can actually conduct spiritually therapeutic conversations in her daily contact with individual patients.

GRANGER WESTBERG

The University of Chicago
February, 1955

[7]

Contents

Part I

The Nurse and the Patient

CHAPTER 1

The Nurse's Task

A THOUGHTFUL nurse recently said, "When people come into the hospital, we see what they are really like. Some of them do a good deal of serious thinking, too, about their illness and about life in general. Some become downright philosophical. Some keep asking why this happened to them. Others become cynical and blame God for the predicament they are in. We wish we knew how to be of more help to them at a time like this!"

Every nurse has sensed this need on the part of her patients for more than just physical care. Many of them are feeling that because most patients have no one to talk to about these inner struggles, perhaps the nurse could do something for them. But how?

It is to the "How" as well as the "When" and the "Why" that this book is addressed. We hope that some of the things which are said will encourage nurses to help their patients more than they ever thought they could. The professional nurse has the privilege of being very close to people during those hours when the very foundations of their lives are being shaken. Her own sensitivity to human suffering in its many varieties makes it impossible for her to treat people with cold scientific objectivity. It is because the writer in his ten years as a hospital chaplain has seen this "extra" care which some nurses instinctively give that he has decided to pull together in book form some of the ideas he has gathered from them. He hopes thereby to inspire a deeper understanding of what actually takes place in the patient when the nurse is willing to go this extra mile.

The writer is a Protestant minister and will naturally discuss the subject from that point of view. Yet every effort has been made to eliminate sectarianism. Protestant, Catholic, and Jewish nurses have read the manuscript and their suggestions have helped to make the book of value to nurses of all backgrounds.

Perhaps the best place to start is with the nurse. Occasionally she herself gets sick. When she does, it looms up as something mighty important. No matter how minor the illness, it somehow takes on major proportions when she is the victim. She has an uncanny ability at such a time to remember a patient she once knew who died from this simple disease. In other words, for the nurse or for anybody else, almost any kind of illness can be thought of as a crisis experience, which means that we are forced to stop and deal with it, no matter how busy we think we are at the moment.

When anything like this happens, we suddenly become amazingly self-centered. All of life turns in on us and we ask, "Why did this have to happen to me? Is it serious? Will it leave a scar? Could it possibly be malignant?" As these many thoughts go whirling around in our minds we have difficulty concentrating on anything else. Self-centeredness is good for nothing—unless there is someone around who can haul us up short and force us to take a better look at some of the reasons why we are allowing the world to center in ourselves. There can actually be a good side to all of this, and the nurse can help bring this out.

Let's take a typical patient, whom we shall call Bill Smith, a married man of about 40—that ulcer in 318—for example. Sometimes (not always) a fellow like Mr. Smith in thinking about himself actually sees something he had never seen before, simply because he had never had the time or the motivation to do much thinking.

Today as he lies in his hospital bed with the possibility of surgery any day, he sees that he is not the entirely self-sufficient person he thought he was. It is as if someone had pulled a rug out from under him and now he is sprawled out on the floor, chagrined, embarrassed, angry, and sorry for himself, all at the same time. It happened so suddenly. He was running his business yesterday. Today he is in a hospital bed. He is stunned by the whole thing.

Because the nurse is the person who happens to be at his bedside during these moments when he is wrestling within himself, it is probably to her that he turns for help. What can she do for him?

She replies, "There isn't much I can do except listen!"

That's right. And listening is one of the most important things she can do to help him.

CHAPTER 2

Listening to the Patient

ALTHOUGH IT may be very worth while for a nurse to listen to patients, the average nurse complains that she does not have the time to do this. She rushes about from morning until night and often does not get off duty until long after she is supposed to. How can she possibly do any listening that will amount to anything? Whatever we say about listening will have to be in the context of the usual two to five minute period which is all the time that a nurse generally has to spend with a patient except where it may stretch to fifteen minutes in some situation like bathing a patient.

A great deal can be said in five minutes. More than we realize can be done in this time for the good or the harm of the patient. It is not a matter of length of conversation so much as it is the sensitivity of the nurse who is listening and responding with her whole self. If she listens sympathetically and with a concern for the feelings that are back of the words that people speak, she is actually performing a healing ministry aiding the work of the physician to a degree that cannot be measured. When a person is encouraged to talk about himself in a way that helps him see into himself, then the way is being cleared for the healing forces to do their work.

Is there an art to listening? Indeed there is. Some

people listen with their ears only. Their minds are a long way off. This kind of listener is not really interested in what the patient is saying, unless it reminds him of something he would like to say. He can hardly wait until the patient pauses for breath so he can get his own life history into it. This is the sort of "listening" so prevalent among the visitors the nurse sees in the hospital every afternoon. They are really not listening to the deep feelings the patients may be expressing. It is merely an "I'll listen to you if you'll listen to me" arrangement and "Hurry up with what you are saying so I can talk."

Most people hear just words. But if the nurse believes that there are meanings and feelings behind every word spoken, then she will begin to listen to far more than just words. When she has been around sick people a long time, she unconsciously develops the ability to read into the words deeper meanings than are apparent on the surface. When a patient says, "This isn't a very serious operation I'm to go through, is it?"—the nurse knows that for him it is much more serious than he cares to let on. He puts it this way because he is trying to talk himself out of being afraid. Here the nurse finds herself in the presence of a fully grown man who ordinarily is quite capable of taking care of himself, but who now in this moment of anxiety, which sometimes borders on panic, is not doing too well at muffling his cry for help. This is really what it is, and the nurse recognizes it as such.

The words people speak in times of crisis are heavily freighted with meaning. How they say things, when and in what context, can speak volumes about themselves. The nurse who listens in a way that allows her to respond to the deeper emotions which are charging the atmosphere will have more significant things to tell the doctor than simply, "The patient had a poor night." She will have insights into underlying feelings that contributed to the "poor night."

Our patient, Bill Smith, is the hard-driving, friendly, fast-moving salesman type. He puts out a stream of chatter that would cause the average visitor to suppose this hospital stay is for him "just one of those things." But the nurse senses that it is much more than that. This is far too serious a blow to his whole way of life to be shrugged off so lightly. He has been talking to her about Northern Wisconsin and vacations and hunting, when out of a clear blue sky he asks, "Do people ever really get over ulcers?"

The nurse has a choice of many different things to say. There are no "right" answers to memorize for moments like this. She has to be herself always and reply in a way which seems most natural to her. But suppose she says:

Nurse: "Of course they do. Now you just forget such silly talk."

Mr. Smith: "But I can't help thinking about it."

Nurse: "You just forget about it and think about hunting and fishing."

The nurse's purpose in such a reply is to minimize his worrying, get him off the subject of his illness and himself. Her motive is kind, and with some patients this is all that needs to be said. Yet for many patients there is *no one* who comes into the room during their entire hospital stay who takes this part of the patient seriously. Everybody tells him to "forget it" or says, "Don't lie there thinking about it." Each time someone says this, it is like slapping the patient's face for thinking such a deep and important thought. No one really wants to deal helpfully with the real man down inside. Everyone is perfectly willing to be with him as long as he kids and joshes, but just let him get dead serious and everyone runs for shelter. He is not fooled by this and it actually creates deeper anxiety, because he now suspects that because no one will talk seriously with him, his problem must be much worse than they are letting on.

When a patient asks a serious question from out of the depths within him it is to be hoped that the mature nurse will be able to help him find expression. He is not asking for "yes" or "no" answers. He knows that no other human can predict what is in store for him during the years ahead, and he is not asking that they should attempt to do so. All he is asking is that someone go down into the valley with him for a few minutes and try to understand what he is going through. Above all this is a lonely experience, and he pleads for friendship and understanding. He senses that this will strengthen him for any ordeal he has to face. If he sees that no one cares enough about him to spend five minutes "feeling with" him, he suppresses all his hostile feelings against everyone and life itself and puts on a false front. One of the reasons so much prattling goes on in hospital rooms is that the patient, after putting out several tentative feelers to those around him, has decided that no one cares enough about him to listen to his deeper thoughts. We may even think that our flippant, superficial replies are helpful because the patient does not bring up such subjects again. We must not be deluded into thinking that thereby we have dissolved the fear. We may have forced it underground where it may fester and do untold damage to the healing powers of the body.

If the nurse could be an invisible visitor and go into Mr. Smith's sickroom with a particularly capable and understanding nurse, she would see some rather different things happen. This man, who ordinarily is so loud and buoyant, within a few minutes confides to her, "They can't kid me that this illness is not serious. They keep telling me to 'forget it' or to 'go fishing,' but I know there is much more to getting over this than just eating the right food. In fact, I have a suspicion that some of the things that have been happening between my wife and me for the past five years have contributed to this upset."

The conversation goes on and Mr. Smith, with the help of the kind of responsive listening that can be described as therapeutic, begins to get some new insights into the possible causes of this illness. And even if the experiences he is bringing out are totally unrelated to the illness as such, nevertheless he is now using this crisis to take a look at himself in relation to his family, his work and his faith, or lack of it. This gaining of significant self-understanding can happen even to blustery fellows like Bill Smith if they are given half a chance. To aid a patient in accomplishing this, need not require the services of a professional counselor. Nurses who have a genuine concern for the deeper needs of people and whose conversations are "Patient-centered" rather than "nurse-centered' can do much more than they may imagine.

Let us take another look at this same conversation in retrospect. How might the nurse have brought out other feelings?

Mr. Smith: "Do people ever really get over ulcers?"

Nurse: "At the moment, because you feel so wretched, you wonder how people ever do, is that it?"

Mr. S.: "That's right. Maybe it is because I have read so many gloomy articles about ulcers. They say that once you have had them, you have to change your whole way of life."

Nurse: "And this is not a very pleasant thought."

Mr. S.: "It certainly isn't. I don't know why it had to happen just now when I am in the midst of reorganizing my business. Things were just starting to look up when this happened. This is going to throw a monkey-wrench into everything I have dreamed of accomplishing."

Nurse: "So as you lie here in bed all these things keep going through your mind."

Now the conversation has possibilities of going somewhere. She has been dealing with his feelings—particularly his negative ones. He senses that this girl understands something of what he has been going through since his sudden acute ulcer attack. He no longer needs to play-act in front of her. He can be himself with her. Actually, she did not help him because of any superior knowledge she has about ulcers. In fact, in this introduction to a worth-while conversation, she did not *tell* him anything new.

But she *did* reflect his feelings. She did not say whether they were right or wrong. She merely accepted them for what they were. She did not fall into the trap of arguing with him or preaching to him.

At this point we should say something about arguing with patients. Here is a nurse who did. As she is about to give morning care to Mrs. Winthrop, a lady sixty years of age, she says,

Nurse: "How are you this morning, Mrs. Winthrop?"

Mrs. W.: "Oh, pretty fair."

Nurse: "Are you from this city?'

Mrs. W.: "Yes, I live on the west side. You know, it's terrible how that district has deteriorated since those foreigners have been moving in. They just ruin everything."

Nurse: "But, Mrs. Winthrop, they have as much right to live where they want to as we have. It is this race and class prejudice which gives America such a black eye. We must learn to live together!"

Mrs. W.: "Have you ever had them move in next door to you and ruin the neighborhood so that *your* property goes way down in value?"

Nurse: "No, but it's the principle of the thing." Etc., etc.

This is a picture of two people getting nowhere. Each has her own point of view and is not interested in what the other person is saying. As the tempers rise, so do the voices and the blood pressure. This is not a helpful conversation, for neither is trying to understand the other.

Does this mean that the nurse always agrees with whatever the patient says, even if it is far from the facts? Of course not. We are only suggesting that the nurse respond to the feelings back of the words of the patient and try to show thereby that she appreciates something of the background out of which this idea or attitude grew. The nurse may not agree with the person's thoughts, but she admits that this person has a right to think as she does. This attitude the nurse must convey by her answers or responses.

Let's conjecture what would have happened if she had:

    a.   listened intelligently to what the patient had to say;

    b.   tried to sense the feelings which were back of the words;

    c.   then replied by reflecting upon what she thinks the patient is really saying.

Mrs. W.: "I live on the west side. You know, it's terrible how that district has deteriorated since those foreigners have been moving in. They just ruin everything."

Nurse: "Things have changed a lot since you first moved there."

Mrs. W.: "Yes, and it breaks my heart after the way my husband has worked on our property trying to increase its value. Some foreigners moved in next door, and within a year, I wish you could see how they have run things down. Now our property has gone way down in value."

Nurse: "They seem to have quite a different standard of living from the people who used to live in that house."

Mrs. W.: "They certainly do. Maybe it is because they've never had permanent housing before. I know I should not talk like this, but I just can't help it because it has upset me so."

The nurse in this case showed a type of understanding which did not put Mrs. Winthrop on the defensive. It did not degenerate into an argument. It was a conversation, and maybe it could develop into a helpful one.

Experiences like this make us believe that *nurses can have meaningful and helpful conversations with patients even though they last only two to five minutes.* We know that they are busy and always on the run, but good nursing care requires that the nurse respond to more than just the superficial chatter of the patients or to his calls for care of his physical needs.

We hope that the nurses who read this will not say that they are going to try out some of these ideas sometime when they are "specialing." None of these suggestions requires that the nurse spend several hours daily with one patient. They simply assume that she get down to what concerns the patients more quickly and thereby waste less time on small talk which leads nowhere. Patients have many significant things to say to the nurse if they are given half a chance to say them.

The nurse's task requires that she care for the whole patient. She cannot serve people effectively if she operates on the assumption that man consists of two parts, that is, *a* body and *a* spirit. A person is one, and she must minister to this oneness, or to the whole person. In the next chapter we are going to have something to say about this "wholeness" of man and how it is related to good nursing care.

CHAPTER 3

The Needs of the Whole Man

IN SCHOOLS of nursing a great deal is being said about the psychosomatic approach to illness. "Psychosomatic" is a word which particularly interests ministers. In Greek classes, it was drilled into them that the word "psyche" really means "spirit," "breath of life," or "soul." A less important meaning of the word is "mind." The word "soma" means "body." The generally accepted meaning is "mind-body" approach to illness. Ministers have no objection to using the word "mind," except that they want to be sure that in this context "mind" includes the spiritual aspects of man, too.

Nurses will find that many people in the fields of psychology and medicine are willing to say that "psyche" has a broader meaning than formerly. The word "psychosomatic" is not even hyphenated, which points up the fact that any approach to illness ought to take into account that a person can never be split up into two parts—with the doctor taking care of the body and the minister dealing with the spirit. The two are inseparable. Many doctors are stressing that they cannot practice good medicine without also being conscious of the patient's inner needs. Ministers learn from experience and from the example of Jesus that they can never think of people as if they were just souls—unattached—for Jesus was always alive to the needs of the whole man.

The body can never be sick by itself, nor the psyche by itself, because man is one. Spirit means, in fact, the whole man. That is the way we are made, and we had better face it.

The nurse is in a unique position. She is a very necessary assistant to the doctor and at the same time, whether she knows it or not, she *can* be a very valuable assistant to the pastor.

The nurse spends years learning how she can assist the doctor, but how does she go about assisting the pastor or chaplain?

Let's go back to the man we called Bill Smith who is in the hospital with a severe case of ulcers. The usual course of treatment is to get him on a good diet with the usual pharmaceuticals, sedatives, etc. This is somatic treatment and very necessary. But all the while, Bill is still stewing inside. He has read that ulcers are often brought on by an overdose of emotions. He is not sure just what this means. The chances are that no psychiatrist will be able to spend time with him explaining this relationship either. His doctor has told him he had better "slow down" and "take it easier," and not worry so much. Bill is willing to accept this advice, but he is sure there is more to it than just taking it easy. The nurse who wants to help Mr. Smith so that he will not have to come back again in a few months can actually help him gain insight into his problem by having worth-while conversations with him. He has now come to the place in his thinking where he is ready to explore to what extent this ulcer flare-up was his body's way of *shouting,* "ouch!" Maybe he was eating the wrong foods. But there is just as good a chance that he was thinking the wrong thoughts. She has explained to him that his body might be acting as a sounding-board for his "inner man" and much like a railroad crossing light is flashing the signal, "Stop—Look—Listen."

Bill is very much aware of the "stop" aspect of this experience. He has been stopped cold and he does not like it at all. Yet he is willing to go along with the nurse on the theory that we all need to stop and rest now and then. She has explained to him that we are so made that when something goes wrong with the body, such as stepping on a nail, a sensation of pain immediately goes to our brain and we *stop* at once to investigate. She has even suggested that we should be grateful for pain. Without it our bodies would quickly waste away, for we would not have "sense" enough to stop to do something about the infection.

The question is, having stopped, is Bill now willing to "look"— and in this case is he willing to look in? No one likes to take such a careful inventory of himself if he can possibly avoid it, and Bill is no exception. But when this nurse who is taking such a personal interest in him encourages him to do it, he thinks maybe he ought at least to have a little look. Now that he is in a hospital he has more time to think than he has had in a long time. After all, he is lying on his back; there is no place to go and very little to do. There is really only one place to look, and that is up. He senses that this experience offers an excellent opportunity for thinking about his faith and its relationship to his life. He has often given this matter a fleeting thought and has promised himself that someday soon he was going to do something about it. He is glad for her encouragement and some suggestions in this self-examination, because he will easily be discouraged if he has to do it all alone.

Then what about this matter of listening? Bill has no idea what he is supposed to listen *to*. The nurse should remember that Bill will listen only to those who have something to say specifically to his own particular needs. He will listen with his outer ear to the advice of the doctor, but whether he acts on it depends upon the doctor's ability to deal with and prescribe for Bill's real needs. Bill may listen with his outer ear to words of encouragement spoken by the doctor, the nurse, or visitors, but these will help him only if at the particular moment he is sufficiently far along in his own inner struggles to be ready to take the steps that are required of him.

What the nurse needs to remember is that Bill will listen with his "inner ear" only to that which speaks to a deep need within him. Whatever is said to him has to be said in response to expressions of his own feelings or he just won't hear it. This is what he wants more than anything—to feel that he is understood and that the nurse is talking specifically to him—not to just any ulcer patient. It is, then, the nurse's privilege to work with people who have been stopped in all their activities, who may be in the mood to look in and, having begun such introspection, to listen to those who might suggest new ways of handling the problems that face them.

Bill and all patients like him take very seriously what the nurse says. They are, in fact, almost wholly dependent upon the nurse while they are in the hospital. Her work is surrounded with a special halo because the doctor works through her and by doing what she says they hope to get back their health. They are willing to do almost anything the nurse suggests if they have found that she:

    a.   tries her best to put herself in their place and is willing to accept them despite their irritability;

    b.   is personally concerned about their welfare;

    c.   has a type of wholesome maturity that tends to rub off on her patients;

    d.   is stabilized by her own faith and has a warmth of spirit that makes hope and faith contagious.

Time and time again patients say, "My *nurse* told me this!"

In other words, "It *must* be true." Within themselves they feel that because she deals with so many people and has such broad experience with so many people in the same condition, it is worth their while to listen to what she says.

If sick people lean on her words with such confidence, she does well to check her own inner life to be sure she has something worth saying and worth living by.

If the nurse agrees that Mr. Smith ought to take advantage of this temporary forced stop to take inventory of himself, then how is she going to help him do so?

If the nurse is willing to think of herself as a member of a doctor-nurse-chaplain team, she now looks upon the hospital as more than just a repair shop for sick bodies. She knows that most patients receive adequate physical care, but she is not so sure that this care takes into account the whole person in a Christian way. Here are ways some nurses have gone about the job of helping patients see the need for looking inward.

This patient, Jim Adams, is a young fellow in his late twenties. This is his third hospital day.

The nurse is giving him morning care. She notices some books on the bedside table. One book catches her eye.

Nurse: "Is that the new translation of the Bible you're reading?"

Mr. A: "Any day I read the Bible would be a lost day."

Nurse: "How come?" *(without emotion).*

Mr. A.: "Reading the Bible is a waste of time. It's just a lot of hokum."

Nurse: "Oh?"

Mr. A: "Yeah, anybody with sense doesn't believe in God. That stuff is for people who can't get along by themselves."

Nurse: "Oh. *(with a smile)* I rather like reading the Bible." *(She finishes her duties and the conversation ends on this friendly note.)*

This much of this conversation was used in a class of student nurses one day. Without knowing what this particular nurse had said in reply to Mr. Adams, they were asked to write down quickly what they would have said if they had been in this situation. See what you think of the following three answers.

Nurse: "Is that the new translation of the Bible you're reading?"

Mr. A: "Any day I read the Bible would be a lost day."

Nurse A: "Do you realize you are talking about God's Word?"

Nurse B: "I think it is disrespectful for you to talk that way about the Bible."

Nurse C: "What you need to do is to *read* the Bible. Then you would soon change your mind."

It is obvious that these student nurses are shocked by his reply and they do not hesitate to show it. It is possible that the patient's remarks here were meant to shock the nurse in the first place. There is nothing that a person of this patient's temperament enjoys more.

Now see what happens as the conversation continues.

Mr. A: "Reading the Bible is a waste of time. It's just a lot of hokum."

Nurse A: "You must be an atheist, talking like that."

Nurse B: "If you would read it with an open mind, you wouldn't find it a waste of time."

Nurse C: "But God says we should search the scriptures. Psalm 119 says, 'Thy word is a lamp to my feet, and a light unto my path'."

Some fifty nurses had written replies in the study of this case. You can be sure that a very animated discussion followed. While each answer was slightly different, the student nurses agreed that most of the replies would fit into one of two classifications, "unhelpful" and "helpful". The largest number were preachy, argumentative, and unhelpful in what they said. They did not seem to be interested in Jim as a person; they were just replying to a threatening statement. They felt that the only way to reply to a religious problem was with an obviously religious answer. The second group of replies were found to be understanding and *helpful*. By this we mean that these nurses were willing to accept the fact that Mr. Adams had a right to his own opinion. Their answers went something like those of the original nurse who first described the incident. They were long on reflective "oh's" and short on "telling him off" or "advice", not because they did not think he needed it, but because he wasn't ready for it. They were interested in learning first of all how he had come to such a point of view. Once they knew this, then they would be able to talk more intelligently with him about it, but they certainly were not going to condemn him without knowing anything about *him*.

In case after case presented in class it became clear that when a nurse argues or preaches, she simply causes the other person to build up his defenses. As long as he feels she is on the "outside" pointing her finger at him, he will not let her in. She will never find out what he is really like underneath. He will not trust her because he cannot be himself in the presence of a self-righteous person.

Quoting Bible verses to this type of person would be of little value. Does this mean that the Word of God does not have power to get under a man's skin? It certainly has! But the nurses who would have preached at him were actually hurling only words at him. Though these words were religious in sound, they lacked entirely a tone of Christian understanding and acceptance. A nurse can suggest helpful Bible verses only after she has demonstrated her genuine understanding of the person so that he knows that she respects his right to feel as he does. This is a democratic principle which we ought to be able to grasp without any trouble. Yet it is one of the most difficult attitudes to cultivate when it comes to someone else's religious convictions. We want others to respect our point of view, but we are not convinced we should respect theirs.

Let's go back to the original conversation with Jim Adams.

Actually all that the original nurse said was, "How come?" "Oh," and "Oh, I rather like reading the Bible."

Some people would say that she certainly was not witnessing to her faith in the best possible way. But to give a "verbal witness" at the wrong time and in the wrong spirit would have done tremendous harm. This nurse, by not being shocked, by keeping her composure and by allowing a little humor to enter in, took the bite out of the patient's words. Notice that she was *not* devastating in her remarks. She did *not* "tell him off." She did *not* cause him to lose face. She did *not* make it difficult for him to express his feelings again at a later time. He could be himself around her, and he sensed that she would like him no matter how contrary he was. From now on he might even be able to express some positive feelings about religion with this nurse because he no longer needs to keep defending his anti-religious position.

It is of some interest that the following conversation took place with Mr. Adams the next morning:

Nurse: "Good morning, Mr. Adams. How are you this morning?"

Mr. A: "Feel rotten. Didn't sleep well last night."

Nurse: "That's too bad. Did your cast hurt?"

Mr. A: "That, too, but I kept having wild dreams all night long."

Nurse: "Oh? What were they like?"

Mr. A: "I dreamed I was alone on a life raft in the middle of the ocean at night. It was very hot. I did not have any oars, so I had to use my arms. Away off in the

[33]

distance I saw an island. I headed toward it and what a job it was rowing to it with just my hands. I finally got there. Just as I started to put my foot on land the whole island with an awful noise was swallowed up by the sea and sank out of sight. I was left all alone. Oh, nurse, it was terrible."

Nurse: "I'm sure it was."

After reading this dream we asked the nurses in the class to comment on their reactions. These were some of them:

"It looks to me like this fellow didn't have anything very solid to build on."

"He must be rowing through life right now all by himself, and nobody will even give him a pair of oars to help him."

"He seems very lonely. He needs sympathy, not argument."

"His agnostic statements seem to be just a cover-up for a lonesome little boy underneath."

"I did not realize there could be such a pathetic story back of this brazen front. Maybe we ought to remember that people like this are really anxious and lonely and need love, not an argument."

"He doesn't know where he's going. He has no goal in life."

The second dream Mr. Adams related to this nurse was also significant. He said, "I had another dream. I dreamed I was back home on the farm. My father and my brothers were all there. It was summer and the sun was shining brightly. We were going home after mowing hay all morning. But for some reason, we had to cross a little bridge on which there was a toll station.

My father and brothers paid their toll and went on through. I couldn't find my wallet and so I called after them, but they paid no attention to me. I shouted at them again, but they pretended not to hear. Then I ran back to the field to try to find my wallet. I was searching all around when suddenly the sun set, leaving me all alone in the field in total darkness. I woke up in a cold sweat."

If there is anything to dreams at all, and if these dreams in any way describe some of the inner problems of this man, then they serve to remind us that a patient may appear composed on the outside while he is very much disturbed on the inside. His undue anxiety may be present because no one has ever helped him get at the basic causes of his troubles. Consciously he may not be aware of this, but unconsciously it may be there in sufficient force to make him wish that someone would respond to him in such a way that he could pour out his true feelings of loneliness without losing face for all his previous bluster.

This puts the healing arts squarely where they belong, for the work of the healing arts is tightly interwoven with religion. To attempt to practice medicine and nursing as if they were pure sciences is impossible. They are also arts and as such are intimately connected with the faith both of the healer and the healed.

It is unfortunate that so much valuable nursing time is spent in routine matters while the patient languishes for someone to help him work hard at the cause of the difficulty. Many nurses say that their instructors have advised against conversations that go beyond simple nursing situations. They say it has long been the rule that nurses are simply automatons who follow the doctor's orders to the letter and never speak unless spoken to regarding insights they might have gained from being close to the patient. This situation is gradually changing and many doctors now admit that it is frequently the nurse who gives them helpful clues as to how they might best proceed with treatment.

Chaplains surely can attest to the value of nurses in helping to discover in patients deep-seated spiritual problems that otherwise would have been missed. Because we believe that every Christian person has a responsibility to witness to his faith and is in a real way his brother's keeper, new stress is being placed on the doctrine of the priesthood of all believers. Every nurse is in a sense a minister. Therefore she will include in her nursing care the care of the whole man. She will be as sensitive to spiritual pain as to organic pain. She will not walk away from spiritual suffering, because she knows that there are ways she can help to relieve it and assist in turning suffering into a growth experience.

Some nurses think they are doing the patient a favor by subtly converting a serious conversation into a humorous one. There are times when this is exactly what is needed, but not always. There are times when serious conversation should remain serious and the nurse by helping to keep it on that level can help the patient to discover thoughts he never knew he had. The nurse may not be able to give as many baths or back-rubs when she takes time for this kind of care, but she will experience a greater feeling of accomplishment. With the coming of practical nurses and nurses aides we hope the graduate nurse may be able to spend more time giving of herself in this fully rounded type of care. The Church should be more aware of the unusual kind of witness which can be carried on by the many consecrated nurses who are so close to the great crises of life. Perhaps we have not begun to make clear the spiritual responsibilities that nurses can so well shoulder. It may mean that we should revise our conception of the role of the nurse and what she can accomplish in what the church calls personal evangelism, that is, helping people to receive the healing riches of the Gospel.

We are happy to notice an increasing recognition on the part of hospitals that patient care must not be limited only to physical needs. It is always a *person* who comes into the hospital, and usually in part because he was unable to stand up to daily demands on him on the outside. With him come all his personal problems, which are often closely related to his illness. As a result the members of the hospital staff know that they inevitably become involved in more of this man than hospitals were traditionally set up to handle. By the very nature of the care which they are seeking to render, they are now coming to see that the hospital's original relationship to the Christian community is significant.

Perhaps the most dramatic description of this new interest the hospital staff is showing in the whole person is in cases of attempted suicide. Until recently when such a patient was admitted, everyone worked diligently to pump out the stomach or sew up the artery. Then in two or three days the patient was released. No one bothered to find out *why* the patient had attempted suicide. Many doctors felt that their responsibility ended with taking care of the body. The patient was now "well" again. At least he was well enough to go out and perhaps do the same thing over again, or live a depressed existence because this tragic and unexplained experience was left hanging over his head.

In recent years a number of doctors routinely call in a psychiatrist or social worker or minister to talk with patients who have attempted suicide. In such conversations the patient, often for the first time in his life, is given a chance to talk with someone about the most intimate struggles of his life. He has been overwhelmed by a sense of loneliness and futility. No one has ever really shown an interest in him—no one, that is, who was able to bring spiritual, psychological and community resources to bear. Because some personal helper has a continuing interest in him and offers to see him regularly after he leaves the hospital, the patient sees more reason for wanting to live.

When a nurse knows that she is part of a hospital team which demonstrates such concern for its patients, then she tries wherever possible to bring to the attention of the minister or other professional helper those patients whom she feels would benefit by their counsel. The nurse can increase her own degree of helpfulness in this field of total care by attending post-graduate courses in related subjects and by reading some of the increasingly good books in the field of religion and health. As she learns what to look for in people, and as she deepens her own understanding of herself in relationship to God and her fellowmen, she will find many more opportunities for this kind of ministry than she ever expected.

CHAPTER 4

The Value of Religious Literature

WE HAVE been saying that there is more going on within the minds of hospital patients than we usually suppose and that during these trying times the nurse is the one closest to them. The sick room situation offers unlimited opportunities to be sensitive to people during moments when they are facing themselves—and some times more realistically than at any other time of their lives. If the nurse feels that this is the minister's field and not hers, it could well be that the one unique opportunity for self-fulfillment in the life of this patient will be missed. To give encouragement and direction because of the contagious warmth of another human spirit does not require a theological education. The nurse who senses such a need and does something about it is operating within her responsibility as a Christian person. To do less than this is to be insensitive to the basic need of each person to feel that somebody cares about him.

As one patient put it, "I had never done any serious thinking about the meaning of life until I was forced to lie in bed for three long weeks. With the help and encouragement of a mature and understanding nurse, I looked deep inside myself. I was not much pleased with what I found. She suggested some exceptionally good books for me to read on self-understanding as well as on the meaning of prayer and faith. They helped to straighten out my thinking so that instead of going around in circles, I feel that I have made some forward progress."

When a nurse comes upon a patient who expresses some confusion about religious or philosophical problems, it would be helpful if she would suggest some books or pamphlets that might help to clarify his thinking. Such literature must be written simply enough so that the average person, whose reading is limited to newspapers and magazines, will not become discouraged.

Many patients who are under stress decide that this is a good time for them to read the Bible. I have had some interesting experiences with such people. As I was about to enter Mr. Simpson's room for the first time, his chauffeur was just leaving. The chauffeur, in an aside, whispered, "Wait'll you see what the boss just got." I introduced myself to the patient, who said, "Say, I just got a gift from one of my employees. It's a *Bible* and, by Jove, I'm going to read the thing. Might as well admit to you I have never read it. I'm going to start at the beginning and go clear through it."

While I did not think much of the idea of reading the Bible from beginning to end, I didn't want to do anything to squelch his enthusiasm.

The next day when I was on his floor, he spotted me as I went by his room, and called out to me, "Say, Chaplain: I've been trying to read that Bible, but I can't make any sense out of it. The English in it is terrible. I thought it would be interesting, but I'm not going to wade through that stuff. Why, it's the deadest book I've ever tackled. I know now why people don't read the Bible."

This is the attitude of a great many people who try to read the Bible without any guidance. The average person just cannot get the real value of it by reading it from beginning to end.

I suppose you wonder what I answered Mr. Simpson.

I said, "It is hard reading, isn't it? Mr. Simpson, I notice that the Bible you have there is a King James translation. That means the English in it is the English spoken three hundred years ago. Have you seen one of the new translations such as the new Revised Standard Version?[1] These translations make the Bible seem to be written just yesterday instead of so long ago."

He replied, "No, I have never heard about it. Can you tell me where I can get one?"

I found one easily because I always keep a supply on hand. Also, I suggested that he start reading the book of Mark along with Genesis.

A couple of days later when I looked in on him, he said, "You know, Chaplain, that new translation makes all the difference in the world. I'm beginning to get the feel of the book now. The New Testament is much easier for me than the Old. I'm already through Luke. Where do I go from there?"

I suggested that he go on to the book of Acts, to be followed by some of the letters of Paul. Along with this straight Bible reading I recommended daily devotional

[1] The Revised Standard Version, 1946. Others are, An American Translation by Edgar Goodspeed and J. M. P. Smith, or the New Testament by J. B. Phillips.

booklets which helped to clarify many passages which he otherwise would not have grasped.

This experience with Mr. Simpson points up several things.

1. Most people in hospitals do a good deal of reading.

2. They may, at this moment of their lives, be more willing to put aside the reading often characterized as "cheap" and be willing to read deeper, not heavier, but deeper things than usual. The nurse may be able to suggest something of this type.[1]

3. Most people need a modern translation of the Bible to help them understand it. The nurse may be able to suggest booklets, too, which will give additional aid.[2]

Nurses are in a particularly good position to aid in the total growth of the patient. This need not take much time, but it does require that the nurse herself be sensitive to the inner needs of her patients. She should also be sufficiently aware of a number of resources, in this case reading materials, to aid in the total care of the patient.

Occasionally a nurse who is shy may find it extremely hard to pray with a patient or even read Scripture. There is nothing to stop her from suggesting a good book for the patient to read. Or it might be that she knows of a good booklet or tract which has helped other patients. If she can personally recommend such a booklet, she

[1] In the appendix we have included the titles of a number of books and booklets which will serve to suggest the type of reading we have in mind.
[2] *Thy Health Shall Spring Forth* by Russell L. Dicks. Macmillan Company, 1950.
My Faith Looks Up by the same author. Westminster Press, 1949.
"Strength for Hospital Days" published by the Methodist Church.
"Hope and Courage" by the Forward Movement in Cincinnati, Ohio.

might even buy a few of them to have on hand. Then when her relationship with a certain patient has reached a stage where she thinks it would be appropriate, she can offer to bring one to him, explaining beforehand how much it has meant to her. Such a personalized gift from a nurse will mean much to the patient—more in fact than if it had been distributed by a religious worker. This can be something which he takes home as a memento of his hospital stay. Some patients have been known to treasure such a gift for years.

Ministers take a rather dim view of certain types of religious tracts. Perhaps it is because of unpleasant experiences they have had with them. There is the story of the over-enthusiastic religious worker who was going from bed to bed in a large county hospital passing out tracts to every patient in the place. The tracts he was giving out were not in any way carefully selected because of their value to people who were ill. They were just tracts—dealing with assorted subjects. As he came to the bedside of one patient he found him asleep. This particular patient had been very ill and was by nature a very high-strung individual. But the worker, determined not to pass anyone by, left a tract propped up on the patient's stomach, so he would be sure to see it when he woke up. Not long afterward the patient began to waken. He was a little confused anyway by a dream he had just had, when suddenly his eyes fell upon the tract. There in large bold type he read, "Are you ready to DIE?" For this patient it set off a trigger reaction which brought the nurses and interns running to his aid. Naturally everyone blamed his temporary setback on the tract. Something else could have set him off too, but in this case it happened that the tract pulled the trigger.

Tracts are usually written with a specific purpose in mind. They are short and to the point. They can be of great value to the patient, provided they are addressed to his particular needs. The indiscriminate passing out of tracts should not be permitted. Any tract that is used should be carefully selected. Just as a doctor would not think of prescribing the same medicine for all his patients, neither would a pastor think of prescribing the same Bible verse or tract or booklet for all his patients. Of course, it goes without saying that the nurse must never use religious literature which has proselytizing as its goal. The only kind of tracts we are discussing here are those which deal with religion and health and are of value to people of any denomination.

There are many tracts and devotional booklets especially written for hospital use and published by the major denominations.[1] These are not expensive and can be given with assurance for they have passed the careful scrutiny of an editorial committee made up of people associated with hospital work.

When it comes to giving the type of devotional booklets which contain readings for each day of the month, the nurse need not be quite so cautious for these contain discussions of all sorts of subjects and therefore do not deal so pointedly with one particular aspect of life, such as, "Are you ready to DIE?"

What we are saying is that it is better to give the pa-

[1] All denominational bookstores have a supply of these. Nurses may ask any pastor about them. Many congregations would be glad to obtain these free for nurses who could make use of them.

tient one tract, having prepared him for it carefully, than to give a dozen tracts which are unrelated to his needs. Too much religious work done in hospitals has been done in terms of "How many people have you spoken to about Christ? How many pieces of literature have you passed out? How many people have you saved?" This is contrary to the entire spirit of the New Testament and in the long run does more harm than we realize.

It is heartening that religious workers all over the country are rebelling against this sort of quantitive evaluation of their work. They are conscious as never before of how much more they can accomplish in strengthening and deepening the faith of sick people if they are given a chance to get to know each patient personally, accept him exactly as he is, and move with him at his own pace. This kind of personal work resembles so much more the way in which Jesus went about his mission. The energy which religious workers formerly used up in running all over the hospital and in many cases from hospital to hospital can now be put to use in such personalized conversations. Of course, the worker's statistical report does not look as good at the end of the month, but he is much happier in his work for he is no longer just the hospital "greeter" or host.

Throughout this book the theme has been that the nurse is in a strategic position to give care to the total needs of the patient. Even though a patient's pastor comes in for weekly calls, or the hospital chaplain looks in regularly, the nurse can still be a valuable assistant. Ministers appreciate having a nurse, who is tactful and balanced in her views, supplement the pastoral care he gives. He does not feel he has any particular prerogative in the matter of helping people to deepen their spiritual dimensions and is more than happy to have her assistance. He knows she will not take advantage of bedfast patients who do not want to speak of religious matters. The patient has the right to accept religious care or to reject it. What we hope is that Christian nurses will make such assistance regularly available to those patients who respond affirmatively to it.

CHAPTER 5

The Use of Prayer in the Sickroom

WHEN IS it appropriate to pray with a patient? When it is, how should a nurse go about it?

Nurses in some hospitals actually take the initiative, at least in reading Scripture to patients. In certain deaconess hospitals in Germany, for instance, in each patient's room there is a calendar on the wall which has a Scripture verse for each day. As the nurse greets the patient each morning, she reads a Bible verse from this calendar. In some Mennonite hospitals in this country it is customary for the entire personnel (including carpenters, plumbers, administrators, as well as nurses) to go individually, following the morning chapel service, to a patient's room where each person introduces himself and asks the patient for permission to read a short portion of Scripture.

This is the way each day begins in these hospitals. Most patients seem not only to appreciate it but look forward to it and often speak of it as the outstanding thing about the care they received in these hospitals. As long as the patient knows it will not take too long nor in any way be personally embarrassing, he seems to accept it graciously. Of course there are some patients who only tolerate it, while others appear amused, but a few of these have said they never are able to shake from their memories the sincerity of the persons who performed this brief morning rite.

Granted that these two illustrations are somewhat extreme, what about the average hospital where the nurse who is a Christian person would like her faith to make more of an impact on those people whose lives she touches? Is there something which she could do without causing upraised eyebrows on the part of her superiors or the physicians? How can she do something of a religious nature without overdoing it and without causing any embarrassment to the patient?

Let me suggest what might be called the minimum type of religious expression on her part.

Suppose the nurse is working with a patient from out of town who is gravely ill and who says, "If I get well it will be because of the prayers of my folks back home."

There would be no good reason why the nurse couldn't say, "And don't forget that you are included in my prayers, too."

This sort of response comes naturally and yet it carries more weight than she may think because it is a sincere statement of her belief in the meaning of prayer; it indicates that she prays daily and that she has a personal concern for the patient that goes beyond the usual call of duty. But, of course, if she says it, she must do it!

Suppose that late one night the nurse goes into a patient's room in response to his light and finds him very distraught. He wants a hypo, but the nurse has no orders for one. She explains this to him and he says, "I appreciate so much what you are doing for me, but I just can't seem to relax. I have even tried to pray, but I don't seem to be able to get any words to come."

Would it not be very easy for the nurse to say, as she places her hand on his, "Let *me* say a prayer for you. O God our Father, we are thankful that you are always by our side. Help us to remember that you said, 'I am with you always.' In the name of Christ the Great Physician we pray. Amen."

Perhaps she would add a sentence or two more. The length is not too important. By this simple act of worship she has brought God nearer to that man at exactly the moment he most needs Him. How awkward it would have been if she had said at that moment, "Shall I call a minister to see you?" First, it may have startled him, and secondly he would undoubtedly have said, "Oh, no thanks." The nurse, as a helpful Christian friend, can fill a need like this in a way that the patient will never forget.

Following this brief and appropriate prayer, the patient may want to talk a little about prayer or about his family or something else that is important to him. This might quite naturally lead the nurse to ask a question such as, "Has one of the local ministers dropped in to see you?" If he says, "No," she can easily say, "The next time Pastor Blank is on this floor I'll ask him to stop by and say Hello. I have met him several times and he is a very nice person to talk to. You'll like him." When she uses this approach to bring up the idea of a minister coming to call on him, he finds it much easier to accept.

We must get back to the question with which we started this chapter, "When is it appropriate to pray with a patient?" The answer is not a simple one and yet a partial answer might be something like this. A nurse should offer a brief prayer whenever a patient asks specifically for prayer or shows by his actions that he would very much appreciate it. The interesting thing is that almost no patient will make such a request of a nurse whose manner indicates that prayer is not a part of her make-up. The nurse automatically excludes herself from such a request by being the kind of cool, aloof person whose way of working with patients would never suggest such a thing. The patient would no more ask such a nurse to pray than he would the window washer or the noncommunicative plumber. In time of illness a patient seems to develop a sixth sense of special sensitivity. The depths within him are constantly searching for someone else in whom he may find understanding and companionship.

The patient who asks for prayer is usually one who is going through an experience which is of crisis proportions to him. When the pain or the fear is more than he can handle he cries out with emotion, "Nurse, say a prayer for me, will you?" For the most part such a request is handled by saying, "I surely will." And it ends there. We realize that this is a common expression often uttered in the same breath with "Don't forget me." Yet the "pray for me" often has an intensity of "and I wish you would say it out loud right here so that it would give me a lift right now. I just can't seem to pray."

Chaplains hear this expression a dozen times a day and each time they have to decide instantly whether hiding within the expression is a genuine desire for audible prayer. The nurse must recognize that any expression regarding prayer, or God, or the Bible, however flippantly said, may be this person's way of trying to convey to someone his sense of estrangement from God and his desire to be helped back to faith. And suppose the patient really does not mean that he wants an audible prayer said and yet the nurse misjudges the patient's statement and begins to pray a simple prayer at his side. You may be sure that this patient will always remember that the nurse was serious enough in her concern for his total welfare so that she voiced this concern in a meaningful sentence of prayer. It seems that it is better to err on the side of praying than to walk out on a person who might be helped by such a simple act.

The kind of prayer we are talking about is a brief prayer of one to five sentences which grows naturally out of a particular situation. It is spoken in a quiet conversational tone with content that brings a feeling of calm and assurance to the patient. The prayer should not excite or stir up the patient by arousing feelings of apprehension and fear. It should be spoken with a ring of honest awareness of the loneliness and confusion which often casts our souls down, yet with a type of confidence in God that is unshaken.

It should not be necessary to say that certainly no nurse ought to force prayer upon a patient who would be disturbed by it or who has known antagonism to religion in general. The nurse's prayer for the patient ought to fit into the mood of the moment as naturally as straightening the pillow beneath the patient's head.

What about the use of Scripture? Now and then there will be a patient from out-of-town who says, "I miss my minister. At home he used to come in every few days and read Scripture for me because my eye trouble makes it impossible for me to read my Bible."

This statement is all but a formal request for the nurse to read to her. It may require more time than the nurse can give at the moment. Perhaps she could say, "Mrs. B., I'll be glad to read to you after I get off duty at 3:30. How would it be if I came in then for a few minutes?" Without a doubt this patient will eagerly look forward to her return. She knows it is beyond the call of duty for her nurse to come back on her own time to read Scripture for her!

There are many other occasions when a patient would very much appreciate hearing just a verse of a familiar passage of Scripture. The nurse ought to know at least a half dozen such quotations from memory. One or more of these could be fitted into the conversation as she takes care of a frightened patient.

If she could memorize some of the following verses, there will undoubtedly be moments when one or more of them will be very appropriate:

> These things have I spoken to you, that my joy may be in you, and that your joy may be full. John 15:11

> My grace is sufficient for you, for my power is made perfect in weakness. 2 Corinthians 12:9.

> Be strong and of good courage, do not fear or be in dread of them: for it is the Lord your God who goes with you. Deuteronomy 31:6

There is no fear in love, but perfect love casts out fear. 1 John 4:18

Be of good cheer, I have overcome the world. John 16:33

Come to me, all who labor and are heavyladen, and I will give you rest. Matthew 11:28

Cast all your anxieties on him, for he cares about you. 1 Peter 5:7

Why are you cast down, O my soul, and why are you disquieted within me?

Hope in God; for I shall again praise him, my help and my God. Psalm 42:11

Cast your burden on the Lord, and he will sustain you. Psalm 55:22

I sought the Lord, and he answered me, and delivered me from all my fears. Psalm 34:4

In peace I will both lie down and sleep; for thou alone, O Lord, makest me dwell in safety. Psalm 4:8

I lift up my eyes to the hills. From whence does my help come?

My help comes from the Lord, who made heaven and earth.

He will not suffer your foot to be moved, he who keeps you will not slumber. Psalm 121:1-3. See also the following verses.

The Lord is my shepherd, I shall not want. Psalm 23:1. See also the following verses.

Peace I leave with you; my peace I give to you; not as the world gives, do I give to you. Let not your heart be troubled, neither let it be afraid. John 14:27

God is our refuge and strength, a very present help in trouble. Psalm 46:1

The Lord is my light and my salvation; whom shall I fear?
The Lord is the stronghold of my life; of whom shall I be afraid? Psalm 27:1

Wait for the Lord; be strong, and let your heart take courage; yea wait for the Lord! Psalm 27:14

Such quotations spoken quietly and sincerely will mean a great deal to the patient, particularly because they have been spoken by the nurse from whom such a statement of faith and trust is not expected.

Whenever nursing supervisors are asked if they object to nurses quoting or reading Scripture for patients, they usually say that they do not object provided the nurse does not carry it too far. Occasionally they have a nurse who is over-zealous. Then the patient suffers because the nurse is more interested in converting him to her particular brand of religion than she is in giving him good nursing care. This over-zealous approach, of course, is not what we are suggesting.

CHAPTER 6

The Sacraments:
Holy Communion and Baptism

THE NURSE will find that most of her Protestant patients have never thought of receiving Communion except when it is offered at the regular times in their churches. Somehow they have the idea that if anyone suggests having it in the hospital, this must mean that the end is near. For these people Communion is like the Roman Catholic rite of Extreme Unction—a final rite for the dying.

Actually the Lord's Supper should be thought of as a strengthening spiritual food which all Christians ought to receive often and especially in times of illness. Many Protestant patients who have mustered the courage to ask for Communion comment that God seems more real to them when He comes into the sick room through the Sacrament. Because of the myriads of inexplicable meanings which are bound up with this Sacrament, it has the power to rekindle flagging faith and to lift the believer out of the valley of self-centeredness. The vertical dimension is added to their vision and they are reminded once again that God is present in their sick room.

A new appreciation of the gift of God's grace which comes to us through the Lord's Supper seems to be spreading throughout our churches. We find that notices are appearing in church bulletins which suggest that all members who are ill in hospitals or at home should ask for Communion more frequently, and particularly on those Sundays when there are Communion Services in their local churches.

A nurse may hear a pastor say to a patient who is a member of his church, "Next Sunday we are having Holy Communion. As you know, we always want to include our entire congregation in this experience. I should like very much to bring the Lord's Supper to you either following the service or on Monday."

With Communion being suggested in this context, the patient has no undue concerns about his physical condition. Instead, he is reminded by this very act that he is an integral part of the community of believers and this contributes to the lessening of his sense of isolation.

However, the nurse will meet many patients who still do not understand the value of the Lord's Supper in times of crisis and who are too timid to ask for it. She can do much to overcome this reticence. Sometimes through her suggestions or because the patient learns how much the nurse herself values it, he will muster courage enough to request it. Here is the way one nurse brought about a discussion of the subject.

Nurse: *(It is Sunday afternoon.)* "Mr. Becker, I wish you could have been with me at church today. We had such a beautiful communion service!"

Mr. B: "I haven't been to communion for a long, long time because of my illness. It seems I have been sick every time they have had it at our church."

Nurse: "Have you mentioned this to your pastor?"

Mr. B: "No, do people have communion here in the hospital? I thought they did that only if the patient were dying."

Nurse: "Oh no! Ministers are anxious to bring communion to patients. They just usually wait until the patient asks for it."

Mr. B: "I think I'll talk to my pastor about it the next time he comes."

Some Specific Suggestions for Aiding the Pastor in Communion

The nurse will be able to assist the pastor who brings Communion to the patient in more ways than she may think. The next time she is talking with a pastor she might even comment on some of the ideas of this chapter. She could explain to him that she would like to help him make the service more meaningful. Ministers will be very happy to learn of her personal interest. Her encouragement may even bring them into the hospital more often. It is surprising how many ministers dislike making hospital calls and particularly Communion calls because of a few unpleasant experiences they have had with nursing personnel. Therefore anything the nurse can say to ministers which will demonstrate her personal interest in what he can do for patients will be received warmly. If a particular minister should seem to rebuff the nurse, it is probably because he has been on the defensive so long in hospital work he does not quite know what to make of this new attitude which the nurse evidences.

When the pastor comes to the hospital to administer the Lord's Supper, he often goes directly to the patient's room without stopping at the nurses' station. Many nurses have said that they would like the pastor to notify the floor nurse in advance so they can be sure to have the patient ready for him. Both hospital chaplains and nurses can encourage pastors to do this.[1] It should always be made clear to them that the nurse wants a chance to straighten up the room and have the patient looking his best. The service will actually mean more if the patient and the nurse spend some time preparing for it.

Setting up a Room for Holy Communion

From the pastor's point of view the following would be a good room arrangement in a private or even a double room.

1. The *dresser* or a movable *overbed table* or a movable *bedside table* can serve as an improvised altar or Communion table. In the case of the latter two, they should be moved to the *foot* of the bed to give the patient breathing room. In this way the service can be conducted with the minister standing six or eight feet from the patient. This helps to make the room seem like a little chapel with the patient in the pew and the minister in his accustomed place. It also removes the mechanics of preparing the bread and wine to a place where it will not divert the patient's mind from the worship experience. Most of these patients attend churches where they are rarely closer than twenty feet from the

[1] It would be helpful to have a nurse speak about these things at a ministerial meeting. Do not hesitate to ask for the privilege of doing so.

Communion table. It is desirable to create in the sick-room a church-like atmosphere.

2. A *clean, white cloth* (a towel, if necessary) should be placed in the center of the surface to be used. Flowers, if there are any, can be arranged on either side of the cleared space.

3. If it is possible, the *patient should be sitting up in bed.* If the patient must remain flat on his back it might be well to tell the pastor of this in advance so that he may give the wine or grape juice by a special spoon designed for this purpose.

4. The *room should be straightened up* in such a way that no unnecessary hospital equipment is in evidence which might detract from the service.

5. The *door to the hallway* should be *closed* so that there will be a minimum of disturbances. One chaplain has a little white cross which he hangs on the door as he goes into the room so that hospital personnel will know that a service is in progress. The service lasts from five to ten minutes. There are times when it would be help-ful if the nurse could remain in the room during the service to assist in various ways.

6. The *curtain between the beds may or may not be pulled* according to the wishes of the pastor. In large wards it is probably a good idea always to pull the curtain. We are not so sure it is necessary to do so in a two-bed room, particularly when the two patients are quite friendly. The other patient is usually able to "listen in" anyway. It is much better to invite him to feel free to listen in on the entire service. In this way, because he is included in it, the service can have value for him, too.

Some pastors specifically include the other patient in the prayers that are offered and so further cement the feeling of good will between two people who often are of quite different religious backgrounds. The service, after all, contains no secrets which cannot be shared. The fact is that such a service conducted reverently in the presence of a non-Christian may take on a missionary character not usually associated with the service of Holy Communion.

In a ward certain modifications of these suggestions will need to be made. In the absence of a dresser or overbed table, the bedside table can be used as an altar. After removing everything from the top of it, it can be moved to the foot of the bed.

What we have been saying about Holy Communion in the sickroom, either in the hospital or at home, leads to these conclusions;

1.   Christian people are appreciating more than ever the spiritual benefits of Holy Communion in time of crisis.

2.   The nurse can do a great deal to encourage patients to ask their pastor or the chaplain for it.

3.   The nurse by her personal interest in having everything in readiness for these sacred moments witnesses to her own faith in this kind of ministry. This in turn strengthens the faith of the patient.

Holy Baptism

When the nurse is assigned to the maternity floor, there are just a few things she should remember concerning Baptism.

1. Baptism is the visible means through which the Christian is brought into membership in the Christian Church.

2. Within Protestantism there are two major conceptions as to the time of Baptism. A large number of denominations hold that Baptism should take place in infancy. The Baptists, Disciples, and some others who number more than eight million in America, believe that it should take place after the child has reached understanding which usually means after the age of twelve. Any decisions concerning baptism to take place in the hospital nursery should be made on the basis of the particular denominational affiliation of the parents.

3. Roman Catholics believe in infant baptism and require only that the person performing the emergency baptism use the brief form described below and herself be a baptized Christian, either Protestant or Roman Catholic.

4. Jewish people, of course, do not believe in Christian baptism and so we would never baptize their children.

5. In the hospital nursery, if a baby's life is in danger, it is the nurse's Christian responsibility to inquire if the parents desire to have the child baptized. If they desire it, the nurse should call a clergyman to come immediately to baptize the child. If a clergyman cannot be reached, then any Christian nurse may perform an emergency baptism.

The baptism is performed simply by pouring water from the palm of one's hand on the head of the infant three times while saying, "I baptize thee[1] in the name of the Father and of the Son and of the Holy Ghost." This may be followed by the Lord's Prayer and the Benediction. Where possible another nurse or two should witness the act. They should then sign a statement indicating when and where the Baptism took place. This is then given to the family or the parish pastor.[2]

---

[1] It is not necessary that a name be used in baptism.

[2] The Appendix at the end of this book contains a brief comment on preparing Roman Catholic patients for Holy Communion and Extreme Unction.

Part II

The Nurse and the Pastor

CHAPTER 7

The Parish Pastor in the Hospital

AN IMPORTANT question for ministers is, "When is it best for a pastor to call in the hospital?" They want to see their people at a time when they will be of most help to them.

The hospital administrators who belong to the American Protestant Hospital Association, after discussing this subject thoroughly, have said that pastors cannot do their best work when they have to come into hospitals during visiting hours. There is a real difference between a visitor's "visit" and a pastor's "call." He comes for a specific purpose—to give pastoral care. This can best be given only when there are no other people visiting the patient. If the minister wants to talk with members of the family, then he may come during visiting hours. Usually he much prefers to minister to the patient as an individual.

In addition, the pastor's own schedule makes it impossible for him to see all his hospital patients during visiting hours even if he wants to. The city pastor who has ten or more parishioners in hospitals may have them scattered all around the city and in half a dozen different hospitals. The average pastor tries to set aside one or two days a week for his hospital ministry, but often this schedule is disrupted by emergencies which require him to reschedule his whole day. In other words, when a pastor appears at the nurses' desk and inquires about a certain patient, the nurse should keep in mind that he may have traveled several miles to see this patient and still has more patients to see in other hospitals. If the room is "busy" at the moment, this minister will be extremely grateful to the nurse if she will go to the room to see if the patient can be made somewhat presentable. A patient whose bath has just been started can usually be covered up with the bath blanket and a sheet without embarrassment to the patient.

If the room is simply being fixed up for the day, perhaps the worker could go on to another room for the period that the pastor is there. It is most discouraging for the pastor who has a tremendous amount of ground to cover in a day to be told that the room will be busy for some time—this period lengthening into a half hour or more. If the doctor met with such obstacles on his rounds, he would have a difficult time getting his day's work done. The pastor runs into the same problem, but he hesitates to point out this loss of time lest he be thought of as impatient, and some people think a minister should never show impatience.

Once the pastor is in the room, he can give himself much more fully to his ministry if he knows he is not going to be disturbed. We realize that often the nurse does not recognize the visitor as a pastor and for that reason an increasing number of clergymen are wearing distinctive garb in hospital calling. The average pastoral call lasts from five to fifteen minutes, with an occasional "problem session" going on for thirty or forty minutes. When a psychiatrist talks with a patient, he expects absolute privacy for up to an hour. The pastor would like the same privacy but usually not for nearly that long.

If there is a hot wet dressing or a medication which must be applied at a certain moment, the minister will understand if the nurse explains this to him. It is hoped that she will not ask him to leave the room without some sort of explanation, indicating how many minutes she will need with the patient after which the pastor may return. She should treat him with the same respect and give him the same careful explanations she would give a doctor.

It is particularly hard on the pastor when he is in the midst of a serious conversation with a patient to have a maid or someone else come into the room to perform a task which could very easily wait until he leaves. The value of the call ends the moment this other person enters. The pastor naturally is friendly and cordial, and before long a three-way conversation with the maid, the patient, and himself has made it impossible for him to continue in his pastoral role. Just because he is comfortably seated and appears to be happily chatting with the patient, the maid has the idea that this conversation is not important. More often than not, this very relaxed exchange of ideas is developing a type of understanding between pastor and patient which is making it easier for the patient to unload some of his own highly charged feelings concerning his illness. This type of conversation is what is sometimes called a "Protestant confessional," where there is both give and take, and each respects the other's right to be himself. In such a friendly setting the patient is often willing to discuss his most intimate thoughts, and the pastor gets very close to his real needs.

No matter how relaxed the pastor appears to be, he is in this patient's room for a purpose. He has come as the representative of the Christian community and in that capacity he is ministering to the needs of this patient. Anything that a nurse can do to give him a period of undisturbed conversation will aid this purpose immeasurably.

CHAPTER 8

The Chaplain-Nurse Team

IF THE nurse is in a hospital which has a chaplain, she then will have the opportunity of working closely with a minister who is in the building all day and who can therefore give more attention to specific patients whom the nurse might call to his attention. In fact, this is the way most hospital chaplains select the patients they see.

Until recently a chaplain was supposed to see every patient in the hospital. This was a difficult assignment because in a large hospital it would be impossible to say more than just "Hello" to any patient. Suppose a doctor walked into the room of a patient who was in great pain and said, "Good morning. I'm a doctor here on the staff. I see you are in great distress. I could make you very comfortable, but I am sorry that I haven't time. I am required to say 'Hello' to every patient in the hospital, so I'll have to run along."

We can see how ridiculous it would be in the case of a doctor. From a minister's viewpoint, it is just as ridiculous to expect him to accomplish anything of value when such time restrictions are placed upon him. You can see why a minister who has spent many years of his life learning how to minister to people in serious trouble would be frustrated by such a requirement.

Recent studies have clearly shown that a chaplain ought to see a few patients, more intensively, rather than all patients superficially. When he is not under the pressure of having to see too many patients, the chaplain can take the time that is necessary to get to know the patient as a person. The attitude of "I'm coming to see you only because this is my job" can change then into one of a genuine personal relationship. The patient need no longer feel that the chaplain is a man who goes around from bed to bed saying the same things to everyone. He may now come to regard him as a Christian friend who has been willing to become personally involved in his sufferings and is now showing by his words and by his deeds that God actually cares.

The chaplain wants every moment to count for something when he is on the floors of the hospital. One of the reasons he has chosen to be a chaplain is that he knows that when people are in a hospital they are more ready to examine or re-examine the meaning of faith in their total outlook on life. As long as they are healthy they do not take the time to do so. Now they have the time, and many have the desire. That is why the chaplain, as he walks through a hospital corridor, hopes that he will not by-pass anyone who is ready to do serious thinking on matters that count.

The chaplain needs both the doctor and the nurse to help him get to the patient at the right time. This not only saves his time but makes it possible for him to enter sooner into a pastoral relationship with the patient. Otherwise he may have to spend hours and hours passing the time of day with many patients, hoping to happen upon a particular one who needs what a minister has to give.

If the nurse wonders which patients a chaplain can help the most, here are some suggestions:

Types of patients who respond best to pastoral care:

1. One who is lonely and has few, if any, visitors.

2. One who expresses some apprehensions and fears.

3. One whose illness may have some connection with his emotions, or with his religious attitudes.

4. One who is facing surgery.

5. One whose surgery or illness forces him to change his way of living, as in the case of heart patients, amputees, and patients with colostomies.

6. One who seems to be doing more than the average amount of thinking about the relationship of his religion to his health.

7. One whose pastor is unable to call on him, or who has no church affiliation and so would receive no pastoral care.

8. One whose illness has obvious social implications, such as unwed mothers, and those with difficult home problems.

9. One whose illness is terminal.

As a nurse looks over this list, she has no difficulty thinking of patients who fit into each one of these categories. If she can keep these types of patients in mind, she can refer visiting ministers or the hospital chaplain to them.

Day after day the chaplain is indebted to nurses who "keep the minister in mind." Here is the type of thing that happens at a nurses' station when the chaplain arrives. The nurse looks over the list of patients on her floor "with the chaplain in mind." Then she says, "There are three patients I think you ought to see."

She continues, "Mrs. Arnold is a long term patient who has just been moved to the large ward because of lack of funds. This has been a terrific blow to her pride, and she has been crying all night."

"Mr. Benson has been apprehensive ever since he came in three days ago. The doctor is sure that his illness is not entirely physical. Something seems to be 'eating' him, but we cannot get at it. Maybe you can. The doctor suggested you look in on him."

"Mrs. Carter is a young housewife of thirty who has a serious illness which is not supposed to be fatal—at least, not now. But when I was in the room a few minutes ago she did not look very good to me. I wonder if she is going to make it. The nurse's aide is in the room right now starting a bath, but the patient needs to see you much more than she needs a bath. I'll ask the aide to wait."

In this particular case the chaplain went directly to Mrs. Carter's room. She was very weak but nevertheless she was able to carry on a conversation. Her eyes were wide open and she seemed eager to talk. This is a part of the conversation:

Mrs. C: "I'm afraid I am pretty sick, Chaplain. I don't seem to be able to snap back the way I did last time."

Chaplain: "It seems as if it is going to take a little longer this time. And so you are worrying more than usual."

Mrs. C: "I really wonder whether I am going to make it."

Chaplain: "You find it hard to have hope at a time like this."

Mrs. C: "I guess I need a little bolstering" (a tear appears).

Chaplain: "The Lord *is* your Shepherd—God *does* care about you. You know that, but it helps to have somebody else remind you of it."

Mrs. C: "It sounds good to hear you say it."

Chaplain: "So that even though you walk through the valley of the shadows you fear no evil."

Mrs. C: *(Speaking slowly and distinctly)* "Yea, though I walk through the valley of the shadow of death, I will fear no evil."

Chaplain: "To know that the Great Shepherd is with you gives you new strength, doesn't it?"

Mrs. C: "Oh yes, thanks, thanks." (Patient drops off to sleep before a closing prayer can be offered.)

The Chaplain then goes on to see Mrs. Arnold and Mr. Benson.

An hour later he was called back to Mrs. Carter's room by this same nurse who had made possible this meaningful conversation. Mrs. Carter had died without any warning. He waited for the husband and other members of the family who arrived shortly. The husband was dazed by it all. He was particularly upset by the fact that no one of the family had been there when she died. Then the chaplain had a chance to tell him of the conversation he had had with his wife—the last she had with anyone before her death. A change of expression came over the husband's face as he said, "Then she was not really alone! I am so glad you got to talk with her. Thank you. I never want to forget her last words. Tell me them again, will you please?"

This experience took place because a nurse took three minutes out of her busy routine to think carefully about the spiritual needs of her patients. She had quickly evaluated what the most pressing needs were and had decided that, in the case of this patient, physical care was at this moment of less value than spiritual care.

A nurse is constantly required to make on-the-spot decisions like this one. How she makes these decisions will depend upon her own inner convictions concerning what things ought to come first. Any thoughtful patient would choose to have a nurse who knows more than just the mechanics of her profession. He would like to think that the nurse is always aware of his total nature and would never feel satisfied until her patients were ministered to in toto.

The logical conclusion, then, is that the nurse's ability to help the chaplain select the right patients will depend to a large degree upon her own insight into human need. She should keep sharpening that ability by living close to God so that she comes nearer to knowing what the mind of God is. Then she will also live close to people so that she will gain increased insight into how best to serve them.

CHAPTER 9

The Nurse as a Christian Person

EVERY GOOD hospital, whether it is supported by the state, the community or a religious organization, resembles a church. In every community the hospital stands to remind us that the Great Physician, Jesus Christ, lived and that He gave us an entirely new conception of the worth of each individual in the sight of God. We cannot think of hospital work apart from Him. That being true, all who work within it are, in a sense, doing what He has asked them to do. Whether all people who work in hospitals are serving in the spirit of the Master is another question.

If a nurse does her work in the spirit of serving her fellowmen out of gratitude for what God has done for her in Christ, then all the work she does is done as unto Him. She could then think of her work as full-time Christian service, just as much as any pastor, deaconess or parish worker. If her hospital happened to be located in Africa or India instead of America she would automatically be called a missionary nurse. Why then, or how, can just a difference in location change the nature of her work? Dedicated service in the form of nursing care is the "work" aspect of the Scriptural injunction to *Pray* and *Work*. In almost every case it was people who believed in prayer who came to the conclusion that they ought to give *evidence* of their faith by the kind of work a hospital symbolizes.

The typical hospital in the average American community came into being some fifty to a hundred years ago because of some acute need, such as an epidemic. People of that community, inspired by the example of the Master, decided to do something tangible about the need. The history of a number of hospitals shows that the church basement or parsonage was often pressed into temporary service as an emergency hospital. Members of the Ladies' Aid and the Men's Club brought beds and mattresses and blankets and food to take care of all who came. There was a great deal of activity as every member of the church sought to serve in some way or another. The minister acted as "hospital" superintendent and chaplain. When the emergency finally subsided and the patients began going back to their homes, they never forgot that the church had served the community, not only as a house of prayer, but also as a house of healing. If it were possible and practical to have a hospital connected to every church building, it would point up the concern which the Christian religion has always had for ministering to all the needs of man.

As a matter of fact some churches actually continued to conduct "hospitals" in their basements or parsonages even after the emergency had passed. In one such town the parsonage was spacious and so were the hearts of the pastor and his wife. They invited these sick folks to come in. The dining room table became the operating table. Soon the people of this congregation began to see that they ought to give such care to sick people at all times. In this particular town the pastor and his wife moved out of the parsonage, and it became the community's first hospital. The spirit of hospital care grew right out of the congregation's life and was an integral part of that church's service to the community.

We are sorry to say that after a generation or so, the close tie between hospitals and churches was severed. New large and imposing hospital buildings were constructed at some distance from the original churches. Those who had started such hospitals out of a genuine Christian concern for their fellows died out. Their children took the hospital for granted, as if it had always been there. As more people used hospitals and paid for their care, there was less need for support from churches. As hospitals expanded and remodeling took place, the old pictures of the Great Physician which had hung in the lobbies were now out of place. They were removed and somehow no one ever got around to getting new ones. The whole community began using the hospitals and the new generations more or less forgot the labor and Christian concern that went into founding them.

Recently the grandchildren of these founders have been rediscovering that the spirit which motivated those pioneers was not primarily the spirit of science. It was the spirit of Christ, who healed the sick because He could not resist ministering to the whole man in order to bring about the abundant life. This is no ordinary spirit, to be found in all religions. It is unique to Christianity. In a recent English work which has not yet come to the attention of American readers, the author who has done outstanding research in this area says, "Sensitiveness to human suffering, a conviction of the value and dignity of human personality—such insights have come to us from Galilee. It is to this new valuation of human life and personality, *which is found in no other religion,* that we owe the care of the sick and suffering on an extended scale."[1]

India, China and Persia had begun to develop the art of medicine a thousand years before the Christian world. Medicine in those countries with such a tremendous head start should have outdistanced Christian medicine. Instead, their medicine is sometimes still in its primitive stages. A part of the reason for this lies in the fact that the people in these countries did not know Christ, which means that they did not know of his concept of the inestimable worth of each individual. The fact that Christianity stresses that every man is of equal value in the eyes of God has undoubtedly contributed to the advances of scientific medicine in the Christian world. The patient does not need to be a Maharaja or even of the upper caste in order to attract the attention of the doctor. The doctor who practices in a Christian setting has been taught since he was a child that all must be treated with the same respect and consideration.

In other words, whether the nurse realizes it or not, her daily concern about each individual patient in her care is a God-given concern which was made clear to us because Christ lived among us. We believe that the *source* of this concern needs to be described to every succeeding generation of nurses and doctors. One of the greatest privileges which can be afforded a nurse is to practice her art with such devotion to God and man that those

[1] *Man's Search for Health,* P. L. Garlick. London, Highway Press, 1952. P. 20. Used by permission.

whom she serves sense that she works not in her own strength alone. By her spirit of dedication she will point her patients to Him who is the source of health, strength and the life abundant.

CHAPTER 10

Prayers

THE FOLLOWING prayers are meant to suggest what some patients might want to say when they pray, but have difficulty in finding the words. There are three ways in which the nurse may use the following prayers:

1. Copy certain portions on a card or piece of paper, and give to the patient for use as he sees fit.

2. Loan the patient a copy of this book.

3. Read the prayer to the patient changing the "I" to "we" when it seems more appropriate.

PRAYER OF GRATITUDE FOR THE HOSPITAL EXPERIENCE

O my God, never have I felt closer to Thee than now. Lying upon this bed my eyes have searched for the eternal in a way that they have never sought Thee before. I confess that when I was enjoying the glow of good health it was the feeling of self-sufficiency which kept me from Thee. I felt that I could get along without Thee.

Now in my sickness I see life from a different perspective. I recognize how insignificant I am of myself— apart from Thee. My life has centered around physical and material joys as if these were all that life had to give. I have taken little time before to think about the meaning of life or to contemplate on my relationship with Thee my Creator. In the stillness of this room a new dimension has been added to my life. O God, how wonderful Thou art. What richness I now see which before I had hidden from myself because of my fascination with things I could taste or touch or see.

Grant that as my health returns and I once more become engrossed with the things of earth that I may never forget to take time each day to hear Thy still small voice guiding and directing my thoughts and actions. Amen.[1]

PRAYER FOR ONE WHO IS SUFFERING A GREAT DEAL

O Thou Father of us all, I thank Thee for the example of Jesus Thy Son who wrestled with the same problems of doubt and loneliness that I now face. In his moments of agony He, too, cried out, "My God, my God, why?" I confess that there are times when I feel that Thou hast forsaken me, yet the remembrance of His victory over the forces of doubt in the garden of Gethsemane sustains me. I know that Thou art my shepherd and dost accompany me into the valley of the shadow.

Help me to see that when I am distraught by pain or fear, it is I that cut myself off from Thee and the strength Thou canst give. In such moments of loneliness show me how tangible Thou art in Thy Word, in the Sacrament and in Christian friends who care for me.

May I never be tempted to base my confidence in Thee upon my own mood at any given moment. My assurance of Thy love is founded upon Him who walked here among men. His life of service, His teaching about Thee as a loving Father, His sacrificial death and His mighty resurrection have demonstrated once for all that Thou wilt accept me just as I am—even with my doubts.

Thanks be to Thee for this assurance. I accept it with my mind. Help me now to accept it with my whole being that nothing may block Thy healing love from coming to me. Grant me that peace which the world does not understand. All this I ask in the spirit of Him Who was tempted to doubt Thy love, but Who in union with Thee overcame and won the victory.

Amen.[2]

FOR ONE NEEDING COURAGE

Our Father, Thou hast been the source of comfort and strength for all generations. I come to Thee humbly asking for an extra portion of courage for the days that lie ahead. I have always known that this body of mine could not live forever, yet, now that serious problems approach I cannot help but entertain frightened thoughts. Enkindle within me the kind of Christian hope and confidence which speaks of both life and death as being in the hands of a loving Father. May the fetters that tie me to the earth and to earthly hopes alone be broken that the spirit within me may rise above the confines of mortal existence and sense its eternal destiny.

As I seek to lift my eyes above the present perplexing problems, I thank Thee that Thou hast promised to be with me always, never to turn Thy face from me. Thou art here by my side, closer to me than breathing, my guardian and my guide. Knowing that I am not asked to face these problems alone, grant that I may, like Christians before me, accept whatever may come with the determination that it may draw me ever closer to Thee. Whether I live or whether I die, the greatest fact of all is that I am with Thee. Amen.[3]

A CONFESSION OF SINS

Have mercy upon me, O God, according to Thy steadfast love; according to Thy abundant mercy blot out my transgressions. Wash me thoroughly from my iniquity, and cleanse me from my sin! For I know my transgressions; and my sin is ever before me. Against Thee, Thee only, have I sinned, and done that which is evil in Thy sight. Hide Thy face from my sins, and blot out all my iniquities. Create in me a clean heart, O God, and put a new and right spirit within me. Cast me not away from Thy presence; and take not Thy Holy Spirit from me. Amen.[4]

PRAYER FOR NURSES AND DOCTORS

O Thou great physician, we who minister in Thy name are grateful for the skills and knowledge which have come down to us that we might aid in bringing health and joy to so many who suffer. May we never equate health with physical strength alone. May we never in our professional work treat people as if they were merely interesting cases. May our work never degenerate into a job for financial gain.

Help us to see our task as a holy calling requiring a vivid sense of dedication to the alleviation of the suffering of a broken humanity. Use us as Thy instruments to bring about health and wholeness to our fellowmen. In our conversations with those to whom we minister may we articulate our reliance upon Thee that they may always look to Thee as the source of all health and strength. Amen.[5]

AN EVENING PRAYER

O God of peace, who hast taught us that in returning and rest we shall be saved, in quietness and confidence shall be our strength; by the might of thy Spirit lift us we pray thee, to thy presence, where we may be still and know that thou art God, through Jesus Christ our Lord. Amen.[6]

AN EVENING PRAYER

O Lord, support us all the day long of this troublous life, until the shadows lengthen and the evening comes, and the busy world is hushed and the fever of life is over, and our work is done. Then of thy mercy grant us a safe lodging, and a holy rest, and peace at the last, through Jesus Christ our Lord. Amen.[7]

PRAYER OF FRANCIS OF ASSISI

Lord, make us instruments of thy peace. Where there
is hatred, let us sow love;

> where there is injury, pardon
> where there is discord, union;
> where there is doubt, faith;
> where there is despair, hope;
> where there is darkness, light;
> where there is sadness, joy;

for thy mercy and thy truth's sake.   Amen.[8]

PRAYER FOR DOCTORS

O merciful Father, who hast made man's body to be a
temple of thy Holy Spirit, sanctify, we pray thee, all
those whom thou hast called to the study and practice
of the arts of healing, and to the prevention of disease
and pain. Bless their work, that they may be followers
of the Good Physician Christ, and give comfort to those
whom he lived and died to save.   Amen.[9]

A NURSE'S PRAYER

I thank Thee, O Father, for the desire and the
strength to serve Thee through serving others. Forgive
me when I keep myself so busy ministering to the needs
of the body that I forget to minister to the spiritual
needs of my patients. As I rush from one task to another, may there yet be a calmness within me which is
evidence of Thy spirit motivating and guiding me.

Help me to see how important it is that I take time
to pray and to be quiet in Thy presence. May I never

labor under the erroneous impression that my busyness, my good works are winning for me a place in Thy kingdom. May these works be but the result of my gratitude for all that Thou hast done for me. May all that is accomplished through nurses for suffering mankind be to Thy glory, O Thou who art the creator and sustainer of all. Amen.[10]

PRAYERS TAKEN FROM A JEWISH PRAYERBOOK

IN BEREAVEMENT

O God, help us to think of thee in this bitter trial. Thou knowest how our hearts are rent with grief. In our weakness, tested so severely in soul by this visitation, we cry unto thee, Father of all life: give us fortitude to say with thy servant Job; "The Lord hath given; the Lord hath taken away; blessed be the name of the Lord."

Forgive the thoughts of our rebellious souls. Pardon us in these first hours of our grief, if we question thy wisdom and exercise ourselves in things too high for us. Grant us strength to rise above this trial, to bear with humility life's sorrows and disappointments. Be nigh unto us, O God. Bring consolation and peace to our souls. Amen.[11]

Hear, O Israel: The Lord our God, the Lord is One.
Praise be His name, whose glorious kingdom is forever and ever.
I am in thy care O God, when I sleep and when I wake
My body and my soul are thine. Thou are with me, I will not fear.[12]

IN SICKNESS

Blessed be the Lord by day, and blessed be the Lord by night; blessed be the Lord when we lie down, and blessed be the Lord when we rise up; for in thy hand are the souls of the quick and the dead, in whose hand also is the soul of every living creature, and the spirit of every mortal. In thy hand do I deposit my spirit: for thou hast redeemed me, O Lord God of truth. Our God, who art in heaven, proclaim the unity of thy name and establish thy kingdom perpetually, and reign over us for ever and ever.[13]

O God, I am sorely stricken; but in my pain let me not forget thee. Thou art long-suffering and patient; and in thy great mercy thou wilt forgive the murmuring lips and the weary soul.

In all humility I lay bare my soul before thee and ask thy pardon for my shortcomings. A broken and a contrite heart thou wilt not despise.

May it be thy will to aid those who would bring me to a speedy recovery. I thank thee for all the dear ones whose sympathy and care have eased my suffering. Mayest thou answer the prayers of our hearts. Heal me, that I may again praise thy name in the congregation of Israel.

O rejoice the soul of thy servant, for unto thee, O Lord, do I lift up mine eyes. Heal me, O Lord, and I shall be healed; save me and I shall be saved, for thou art my praise. Amen.[14]

ON THE BIRTH OF A CHILD

Almighty God, we thank Thee most fervently for the child with which thou hast blessed our home. Accept our grateful prayers, that through the clouds of anxiety has come the light of a new joy, by which our spirits are exalted and our marriage bond is sanctified anew.

In reverence and joy do we receive this sacred trust. May we be found worthy of thy favor. Help us to fulfill our duties as parents wisely and faithfully, whatever may be the sacrifice.

Let thy blessing rest upon our dear child. Keep it in life, and sustain it in health, that we may rear it for loving service to others and devotion to thee. Amen.[15]

FOOTNOTES

1. Granger Westberg.
2. G. W.
3. G. W.
4. Psalm 51. Revised Standard Version of the *Bible*.
5. G. W.
6. *The Student Prayerbook*. John Oliver Nelson, Editor. Association Press, 1953, p. 19.
7. John Henry Newman.
8. Francis of Assisi.
9. *Prayers in Private Devotion in War-Time*. Willard L. Sperry. Harper & Brothers, 1943, p. 29. Used by permission.
10. G. W.
11. *The Union Prayerbook for Jewish Worship*. The Central Conference of American Rabbis, 1925, p. 375. Used by permission.
12. *Ibid.*, p. 341.
13. *Form of Daily Prayers*. H. Abrahams. Revised by Isaac L. Lyon, 1836, p. 138.
14. *The Union Prayerbook for Jewish Worship*. p. 367.
15. *Ibid.*, p. 365.

Appendix

NOTES ON MINISTERING TO
ROMAN CATHOLIC PATIENTS

A ROMAN CATHOLIC patient is prepared for communion by going to confession. This usually takes place
the night before, when the priest comes in and spends a
few minutes with the patient to hear his confession.
There is no preparation which the nurse need make for
this call, except that the priest will appreciate having
the curtain drawn between the beds.

The following morning the priest usually comes directly from the altar of his church where he has cele-
brated early mass. He carries with him the Blessed Sacrament or wafer in a small gold container called a pyx
which is about the size of a large watch. This is carried
in a pocket over his heart, and it is said that the reason
men tip their hats to the priest is that he may be carry-
ing the consecrated Host. Inasmuch as the Host or
wafer has already been consecrated at the altar, the
service in the patient's room consists merely of "the
distribution."

The patient must, of course, receive the Sacrament
fasting, which means nothing except pure water by
mouth after midnight unless a special dispensation has
been given. The reason for this rule is to make certain
that the first thing which touches the communicant's
mouth that day is the Lord's Supper. The patient is expected to have thought about the Mass prior to the

[91]

priest's arrival, and to have pictured the service in his mind.

The priest asks that the bedside table be cleared and on it placed a white cloth, a glass of water and a spoon. As the priest enters the room he turns to the table, genuflects, takes the Sacrament in his hand, turns to the patient and says, "Behold the Lamb of God, behold Him who taketh away the sins of the world." The communicant responds, "Lord, I am not worthy that thou shouldst enter under my roof but only say the word and my soul shall be healed." The priest administers the Sacrament saying, "May the body of our Lord Jesus Christ preserve your soul unto life everlasting. Amen."

The priest always holds the Host with his right thumb and forefinger for these are the two fingers which were consecrated for this purpose at his ordination. In order to be sure that no part of the consecrated Host adheres to his fingers, he then takes the spoon into his left hand, dips it into the glass of water, places the thumb and forefinger of his right hand in the water to wash off such particles, and then gives the patient the spoonful of water. This is essentially what takes place in the room at the time of a sick communion. A final prayer is spoken and the priest leaves, the whole act taking approximately one to three minutes.

Extreme Unction for Roman Catholic Patients

This sacrament of the Roman Catholic Church has been used primarily in cases of severe illness where the patient is expected to die. In such cases, it is wise that the family be notified that the patient is in critical condition, suggesting that they send for the priest. Most Roman Catholics think of this rite as being the final blessing for a person before he expires.

Extreme Unction, however, actually has grown out of the statement in the fifth chapter of James which states, "Is any among you sick? Let him call for the elders of the church; and let them pray over him, anointing him with oil in the name of the Lord; and the prayer of faith will save the sick man, and the Lord will raise him up . . ."

This implies that this sacrament should not have the negative connotations which it seems now so generally to have. Occasionally one will find a Catholic patient who has been instructed in this positive aspect of Extreme Unction. He may even ask for it during a severe illness because of the strength it can give him. Only one anointing can be given for any one illness, but extreme unction is actually not "the last rite" to be performed only *once* in a person's lifetime. The nurse might find herself in a position where she can explain this aspect to a patient who is frightened by the prospects of the priest coming to give him Last Rites.

A description of the sacrament of Extreme Unction is given in *The Treasure of Liturgy* by Reverend Nicolas Maas. "The priest requests the sick person to elevate his thoughts to God, and inspires him with firm hope of everlasting life. He explains, in short, that Extreme Unction will give him patience and resignation in his sufferings, take away every trace of sin, and if it is God's will, even restore him to health."[1]

[1] *The Treasure of the Liturgy,* Reverend Nicholas Maas. (Milwaukee, The Bruce Publishing Company, 1932) p. 267. Used by permission.

Prayers precede the anointing of the patient. Then the priest dips his thumb in holy oil and anoints the eyes of the sick person, saying, "Through this holy unction and His most tender mercy, may the Lord pardon you whatever sins you have committed by sight. Amen."[2] These words are repeated as the priest anoints each ear, the nose, the lips, and the feet. He then makes the sign of the cross on each organ and limb, and this is followed by more prayers.

NOTES ON MINISTERING TO JEWISH PATIENTS

ORTHODOX JEWISH patients follow special food regulations which prevent them from eating pork, some seafoods, and from having both meat and dairy products in the same meal. Although they are excused from strict adherence to dietary laws while they are ill, they will appreciate the hospital's co-operation in sticking as closely to these rules as possible. For the strict Orthodox Jew the matter of diet is perhaps the most difficult feature of hospital routine. In fact, he often looks upon his observance of his religious laws in such a setting as a test of his faith.

Jewish male children are customarily circumcised on the seventh day after birth. This event is a time of celebration because it marks the entry of a potential citizen into the ranks of his forefathers. The Mohel and other male persons present wear their hats. This is because it is believed to be more respectful to the Lord to keep the

[2] *Ibid.*, p. 269.

head covered when praying or engaging in any religious act.

When a Jewish patient is critically ill, his family usually summons the rabbi. The nurse is not usually responsible for this, unless the patient requests her help in calling a rabbi.

ANOINTING

A FEW PROTESTANT groups are placing increased emphasis upon anointing in time of illness. This is particularly true of the Church of the Brethren and the Protestant Episcopal Church. The minister or priest will bring to the patient's room the necessary material for the anointing. The nurse can assist the officiant by making the patient ready and by providing privacy during the time that the service is in progress.

BOOKS WHICH PATIENTS ENJOY READING

Edmund Babbitt. *Strength for Hospital Days.* Board of Hospitals and Homes of the Methodist Church, 1946.

John Baillie. *A Diary of Private Prayer.* Scribner's Sons, 1949.

Bernard I. Bell. *Beyond Agnosticism.* Harper and Brothers, 1929.

Russell L. Dicks. *My Faith Looks Up.* The Westminster Press, 1949.

Thy Health Shall Spring Forth. The Macmillan Company, 1950.

Nels Ferré. *Strengthening the Devotional Life.* Harper & Bros., 1951.

Harry Emerson Fosdick. *The Meaning of Prayer.* Association Press, 1951.

E. Stanley Jones. *Abundant Living.* Abingdon-Cokesbury Press, 1952.

Thomas Kelly. *A Testament of Devotion.* Harper & Brothers, 1941.

C. S. Lewis. *The Case for Christianity.* Macmillan Company, 1943. *Christian Behaviour.* Macmillan Company, 1944. *The Screwtape Letters.* Macmillan Company, 1945.

James Hasting Nichols. *Primer for Protestants.* Association Press, 1951.

J. B. Phillips. *Your God Is too Small.* Macmillan Company, 1952.

James A. Pike. *Beyond Anxiety.* Scribner's Sons, 1954.

Carl J. Scherzer. *Springs of Living Waters.* The Westminster Press, 1951.

Elton Trueblood. *The Common Ventures of Life.* Harper & Brothers, 1949.